Grammar minutes

100 minutes to practise and reinforce essential skills

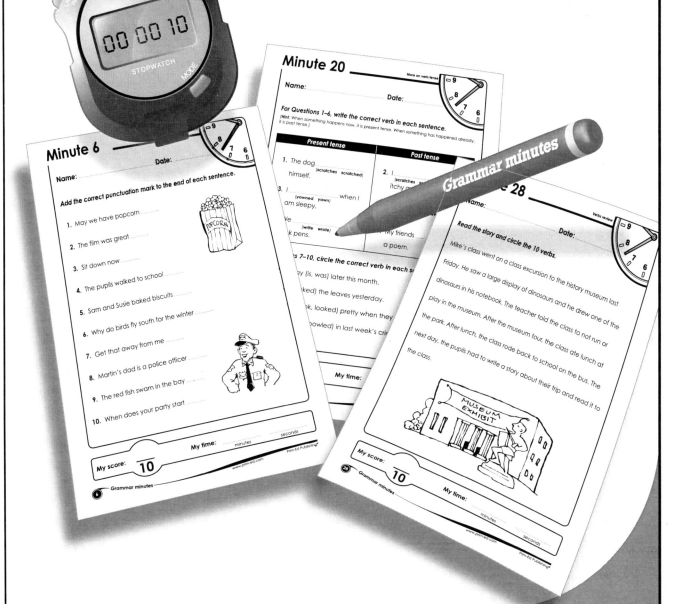

Carmen S Jones

6328

Grammar minutes *Book 2*

Published by Prim-Ed Publishing® 2011 under licence to
Creative Teaching Press.
Copyright© 2009 Creative Teaching Press.
This version copyright© Prim-Ed Publishing® 2011

ISBN 978-1-84654-295-4
PR–6328

Titles available in this series:
Grammar minutes Book 1
Grammar minutes Book 2
Grammar minutes Book 3
Grammar minutes Book 4
Grammar minutes Book 5
Grammar minutes Book 6

Internet websites

In some cases, websites or specific URLs may be recommended. While these are checked and rechecked at the time of publication, the publisher has no control over any subsequent changes which may be made to webpages. It is *strongly* recommended that the class teacher checks *all* URLs before allowing pupils to access them.

View all pages online

Website: www.prim-ed.com

GRAMMAR MINUTES – BOOK 2

Foreword

Grammar minutes is a six-book series for primary school pupils that provides a structured daily programme of easy-to-follow activities in grammar. The main objective is grammar proficiency, attained by teaching pupils to apply grammar skills to answer questions effortlessly and rapidly. The questions in this book provide pupils with practice in the following key areas of grammar instruction:

- *sentence structure*
- *nouns*
- *pronouns*
- *adverbs*
- *punctuation*
- *contractions*
- *capital letters*
- *verbs*
- *adjectives*
- *compound words*
- *articles.*

Grammar minutes – Book 2 features 100 'minutes', each with 10 classroom-tested problems. Use this comprehensive resource to improve your pupils' overall grammar proficiency, which will promote greater self-confidence in their grammar skills as well as provide the everyday practice necessary to succeed in testing situations. Designed to be implemented in numerical order from 1 to 100, the activities in *Grammar minutes* are developmental through each book and across the series.

Comprehensive teachers notes, record-keeping charts, a scope-and-sequence table (showing when each new concept and skill is introduced), and photocopiable pupil reference materials are also included.

How many minutes does it take to complete a 'grammar minute'?

Pupils will enjoy challenging themselves as they apply their grammar knowledge and understanding to complete a 'grammar minute' in the fastest possible time.

Titles available in this series:

- *Grammar minutes – Book 1*
- *Grammar minutes – Book 2*
- *Grammar minutes – Book 3*
- *Grammar minutes – Book 4*
- *Grammar minutes – Book 5*
- *Grammar minutes – Book 6*

Contents

Teachers notes .... iv – viii

    How to use this book .... iv – v

    Minute records – Teacher record table vi

    Minute journal – Pupil record sheet vii

    Scope-and-sequence table viii

Grammar minutes 1–100 1–100

Answers 101–105

Teachers notes

How to use this book

Grammar minutes can be used in a variety of ways, such as:

- **a speed test.** As the teacher starts a stopwatch, pupils begin the 'minute'. As each pupil finishes, he/she raises a hand and the teacher calls out the time. The pupil records this time on the appropriate place on the sheet. Alternatively, a particular time can be allocated for the whole class to complete the 'minute' in.
  Pupils record their scores and time on their 'minute journal' (see page vii).

- **a whole-class activity.** Work through the 'minute' together as a teaching or reviewing activity.

- **a warm-up activity.** Use a 'minute' a day as a 'starter' or warm-up activity before the main part of the lesson begins.

- **a homework activity.** If given as a homework activity, it would be most beneficial for the pupils if the 'minute' is corrected and reviewed at the start of the following lesson.

Grammar minutes strategies

Encourage pupils to apply the following strategies to help improve their scores and decrease the time taken to complete the 10 questions.

- To use strategies whenever possible.
- To move quickly down the page, answering the problems they know first.
- To come back to problems they are unsure of, after they have completed all other problems.
- To make educated guesses when they encounter problems they are not familiar with.

A *Grammar minute* pupil activity page.

Name and date
Pupils write their name and the date in the spaces provided.

Questions
There are 10 problems, providing practice in every key area of grammar proficiency.

Score
Pupils record their score out of 10 in the space provided.

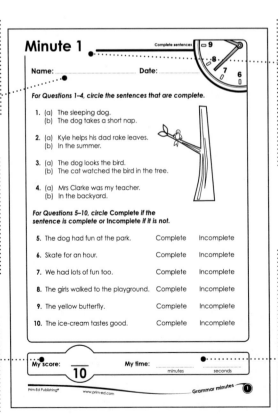

'Grammar minute' number
Grammar minutes are designed to be completed in numerical order.

Time
Pupils record the time taken to complete the 'minute' at the bottom of the sheet. (This is optional.)

Teachers notes

Marking

Answers are provided for all activities. How these activities are marked will vary according to the teacher's organisational policy. Methods could include whole-class checking, partner checking, individual pupil checking or collection by the teacher.

Diagnosis of problem areas

Grammar minutes provides the teacher with immediate feedback of whole-class and individual pupil understanding. This information is useful for future programming and planning of further opportunities to practise and review the skills and concepts which need addressing.

Make use of the structured nature of the questions to diagnose problem areas; rather than asking who got 10 out of 10, ask the pupils who got Question 1 correct to raise their hands, Question 2, Question 3 etc. In this way, you will be able to quickly determine which concepts are causing problems for the majority of the pupils. Once the routine of *Grammar minutes* is established, the teacher will have time to work with individuals or small groups to assist them with any areas causing problems.

Meeting the needs of individuals

The structure of *Grammar minutes* allows some latitude in the way the books are used; for example, it may be impractical (as well as demoralising for some) for all pupils to be using the same book. It can also be difficult for teachers to manage the range of abilities found in any one classroom, so while pupils may be working at different levels from different books, the familiar structure makes it easier to cope with individual differences. An outline of the suggested age range levels each book is suited to is given on page iii.

Additional resources:

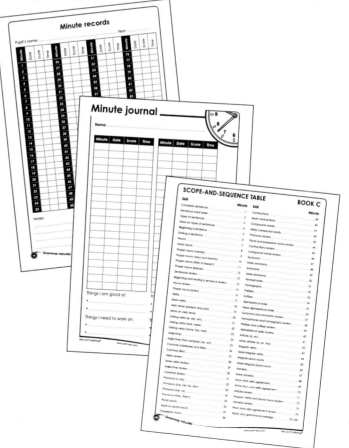

- **Minute records**

  Teachers can record pupil scores and times on the **Minute records** table located on page vi.

- **Scope and sequence**

  The **Scope-and-sequence table** gives the 'minute' in which each new skill and concept appears for the first time.

- **Minute journal**

  Once a 'minute' is completed, pupils record their score and time on their **Minute journal**, located on page vii.

- **Answers to all questions are found on pages 101 to 105.**

Minute records

Pupil's name: .... Class: ....

Minute:	Date	Score	Time	Minute:	Date	Score	Time	Minute:	Date	Score	Time	Minute:	Date	Score	Time
1				26				51				76			
2				27				52				77			
3				28				53				78			
4				29				54				79			
5				30				55				80			
6				31				56				81			
7				32				57				82			
8				33				58				83			
9				34				59				84			
10				35				60				85			
11				36				61				86			
12				37				62				87			
13				38				63				88			
14				39				64				89			
15				40				65				90			
16				41				66				91			
17				42				67				92			
18				43				68				93			
19				44				69				94			
20				45				70				95			
21				46				71				96			
22				47				72				97			
23				48				73				98			
24				49				74				99			
25				50				75				100			

Notes:

....

....

....

....

www.prim-ed.com Prim-Ed Publishing®

Minute journal

Name: ....

Minute	Date	Score	Time

Minute	Date	Score	Time

Things I am good at.

• ....

• ....

Things I need to work on.

• ....

• ....

Things I am good at.

• ....

• ....

Things I need to work on.

• ....

• ....

SCOPE-AND-SEQUENCE TABLE BOOK 2

Skill	Minute
Complete sentences	1
Sentence word order	2
Types of sentences	3
More on types of sentences	4
Beginning a sentence	5
Ending a sentence	6
Nouns	7
More nouns	8
Proper nouns (names)	9
Proper nouns (days and months)	10
Proper nouns (titles of respect)	11
Proper nouns (places)	12
Sentences review	13
Beginning and ending a sentence review	14
Nouns review	15
Proper nouns review	16
Verbs	17
More verbs	18
Verb tense (present and past)	19
More on verb tense	20
Linking verbs (*is, are, am*)	21
Linking verbs (*was, were*)	22
Linking verbs (*have, has, had*)	23
Adjectives	24
Adjectives that compare (*-er, -est*)	25
Commas (addresses and titles)	26
Commas (lists)	27
Verbs review	28
More verbs review	29
Adjectives review	30
Commas review	31
Pronouns (*I, me*)	32
Pronouns (*she, her, he, him*)	33
Pronouns (*we, us*)	34
Pronouns (*they, them*)	35
Plural nouns	36
More on plural nouns	37
Possessive nouns	38

Skill	Minute
Contractions	39
More contractions	40
Compound words	41
More compound words	42
Pronouns review	43
Plural and possessive nouns review	44
Contractions review	45
Compound words review	46
Synonyms	47
More synonyms	48
Antonyms	49
More antonyms	50
Homophones	51
Homographs	52
Prefixes	53
Suffixes	54
Alphabetical order	55
More alphabetical order	56
Synonyms and antonyms review	57
Homophones and homographs review	58
Prefixes and suffixes review	59
Alphabetical order review	60
Articles (*a, an*)	61
More articles (*a, an, the*)	62
Irregular verbs	63
More irregular verbs	64
Irregular plural nouns	65
More irregular plural nouns	66
Adverbs	67
More adverbs	68
Noun and verb agreement	69
More noun and verb agreement	70
Articles review	71
Irregular verbs and plural nouns review	72
Adverbs review	73
Noun and verb agreement review	74
Apply your grammar knowledge	75–100

Minute 1

Name: .... **Date:** ....

For Questions 1–4, circle the sentences that are complete.

1. (a) The sleeping dog.
   (b) The dog takes a short nap.

2. (a) Kyle helps his dad rake leaves.
   (b) In the summer.

3. (a) The dog looks the bird.
   (b) The cat watched the bird in the tree.

4. (a) Mrs Clarke was my teacher.
   (b) In the backyard.

For Questions 5–10, circle Complete if the sentence is complete or Incomplete if it is not.

5. The dog had fun at the park.   Complete   Incomplete

6. Skate for an hour.   Complete   Incomplete

7. We had lots of fun too.   Complete   Incomplete

8. The girls walked to the playground.   Complete   Incomplete

9. The yellow butterfly.   Complete   Incomplete

10. The ice-cream tastes good.   Complete   Incomplete

My score: _____
10

My time: ....
          minutes   seconds

Minute 2

Name: .... **Date:** ....

For Questions 1–5, circle the sentences that are in the correct word order.

1. (a) The snake mud slides the through.
   (b) The snake slides through the mud.

2. (a) The clown makes the children laugh.
   (b) The children makes laugh the clown.

3. (a) The apples in the tree are rotten.
   (b) The tree apples in the are rotten.

4. (a) At beach had the fun Regina.
   (b) Regina had fun at the beach.

5. (a) We went to Malaysia for our holiday.
   (b) For Malaysia we our went to holiday.

For Questions 6–10, rewrite the sentences in the correct word order.

6. Funny film was the. ....

7. I bike my on ride. ....

8. The sleeps lot a cat. ....

9. Sweet the ice-cream is. ....

10. Was puppy the lost. ....

My score: _____
10

My time: ....
           minutes   seconds

Minute 3

Name: .... **Date:** ....

Read each sentence and write the type of sentence it is on the line.
Put T for telling, A for asking or E for exclaiming.

1. Do you have a pencil? ....

2. There are seven days in a week. ....

3. I can't wait until the holidays! ....

4. When is your birthday party? ....

5. My teacher loves green apples. ....

6. Our family is going camping. ....

7. May I make my own lunch today? ....

8. I spilled milk on my dress! ....

9. There are six fish in the pond. ....

10. Tony and Charlie play football. ....

My score: ____
10

My time: ....
minutes   seconds

Minute 4

Name: .... **Date:** ....

For Questions 1–3, circle the correct telling sentences.

1. (a) May we go to the park.
   (b) We are going to the park.

2. (a) Bob and John play basketball.
   (b) Wow, Bob scored five points.

3. (a) The cat climbs the tree.
   (b) Is your cat in the tree.

For Questions 4–6, circle the correct asking sentences.

4. (a) What time are we going to the match?
   (b) The pizza tastes so good?

5. (a) My mother makes the best chocolate cake?
   (b) How are you today?

6. (a) Brenda and Carmen love to go shopping?
   (b) Why do birds fly north for the winter?

For Questions 7–10, circle the correct exclaiming sentences.

7. (a) Chelsea danced in the show!
   (b) Wow, Chelsea was great in the show!

8. (a) You are a terrific dancer!
   (b) I have a dance class on Saturdays!

9. (a) The tree is falling down on our house!
   (b) We have a tree in front of our house!

10. (a) A red car is coming up the street!
    (b) Watch out for that red car!

My score: ——— **My time:** ....
10   minutes   seconds

www.prim-ed.com

Minute 5

Name: .... **Date:** ....

Circle the word in each sentence that should begin with a capital letter and write it correctly on the line.

1. i play football every day.   ....

2. we fly kites at Grant Park.   ....

3. sarah's father makes the best pancakes.   ....

4. wednesday is the day of our maths test.   ....

5. my dad was born in Germany.   ....

6. october is my favourite month of the year.   ....

7. max is my dog's name.   ....

8. greece has a lot of nice beaches.   ....

9. they like to shop at the Oakleigh Markets.   ....

10. every Friday we eat pizza for dinner.   ....

My score: $\dfrac{}{10}$

My time: ....
              minutes   seconds

Minute 6

Name: .... **Date:** ....

Add the correct punctuation mark to the end of each sentence.

1. May we have popcorn ....

2. The film was great ....

3. Sit down now ....

4. The pupils walked to school ....

5. Sam and Susie baked biscuits ....

6. Why do birds fly south for the winter ....

7. Get that away from me ....

8. Martin's dad is a police officer ....

9. The red fish swam in the bay ....

10. When does your party start ....

My score: _____
10

My time: ....
minutes   seconds

Minute 7

Name: .... **Date:** ....

Place each noun (naming word) in the correct box below.

pupil	phone	park	sister	flower
school	radio	teacher	lake	umpire

Person	Place	Thing
1.	5.	8. ....
2.	6.	9. ....
3.	7.	10. ....
4.		

My score: $\overline{10}$

My time: .... minutes .... seconds

Minute 8

Name: ....   Date: ....

Circle the nouns (naming words) in the sentences.
(**Hint**: Each sentence has two nouns to circle.)

1. The girls play in the park.

2. Brandon likes to read scary books.

3. Apples and grapes taste good.

4. Marie and Tina are playing.

5. Tom baked a chocolate cake.

6. The beach is fun during the summer.

7. Chris is looking for his dog.

8. The dog chased the cat.

9. The clouds in the sky are fluffy.

10. Mr Manson is a new teacher.

My score: ____   My time: ....
10   minutes   seconds

Minute 9

Name: .... **Date:** ....

Circle the proper nouns (naming words) that should begin with capital letters in the sentences below.

(Hint: Proper nouns name specific people, places, things, or animals.)

1. meg and amy are sisters.

2. My dog, charlie, is grey and white.

3. I asked nick and mitch to help me.

4. The cat's name is lucky.

5. We named the rabbit in our class punka.

6. Our class saw timothy the tiger at the zoo.

7. The teacher's helper is nicole.

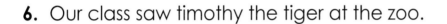

8. megan and madison are twins.

9. I have a bird named mozart.

10. She brought her hamster, bubbles, to school.

My score:

$\dfrac{}{10}$

My time:

....
minutes   seconds

Minute 10

Name: .... **Date:** ....

Circle the correct way to write the days of the week and months of the year.

1. (a) friday
   (b) Friday

2. (a) December
   (b) december

3. (a) august
   (b) August

4. (a) Monday
   (b) monday

5. (a) sunday
   (b) Sunday

6. (a) March
   (b) march

7. (a) may
   (b) May

8. (a) Wednesday
   (b) wednesday

9. (a) Tuesday
   (b) tuesday

10. (a) september
    (b) September

My score: _____
10

My time: ....
    minutes   seconds

Minute 11

Name: ....   **Date:** ....

For Questions 1–5, circle the proper nouns for people in the sentences.

1. Uncle Herbert cut down the tree.

2. My dentist is Dr Dawson.

3. The pupils like Mrs Gomez.

4. Police Officer Edwards spoke to our class.

5. I baked a chocolate cake with Grandma Rose.

For Questions 6–10, circle the correct way to write each name.

6. (a) dr allen   (b) Dr allen   (c) Dr Allen

7. (a) Supervisor Simmons   (b) supervisor Simmons
   (c) Supervisor simmons

8. (a) uncle Mike   (b) Uncle Mike   (c) Uncle mike

9. (a) Ms patrick   (b) ms Patrick   (c) Ms Patrick

10. (a) Principal jones   (b) Principal Jones   (c) principal jones

My score: ____
10

My time: ....
minutes   seconds

9

8

7

6

Name: .... **Date:** ....

Circle the proper nouns for places in the sentences.

1. I went to Erskineville Secondary School.

2. We saw flowers at Parker Garden Centre.

3. Burger Express is my favourite place to eat.

4. My sister works at Pets 4 All.

5. She is from Barcelona, Spain.

6. We had so much fun at Rose Park.

7. The Rope Walk Centre has lots of shops.

8. Australia has the best beaches.

9. I have a library card for the Strath Creek Library.

10. The girls live in Howson Street.

My score: _____ **My time:** ....

$\dfrac{}{10}$

minutes   seconds

Minute 13

Name: .... **Date:** ....

For Questions 1–3, write C on the line if the sentence is complete or I if it is incomplete.

1. We had pizza for dinner on Friday. ....

2. The cute little baby. ....

3. Larry and Barry are singing a song. ....

For Questions 4–5, circle the sentences that are in the correct word order.

4. (a) Ralph is going to the rugby game.
   (b) Going to the Ralph is rugby game.

5. (a) The flowers in her garden likes to water my mother.
   (b) My mother likes to water the flowers in her garden.

For Questions 6–10, read each sentence and write the type of sentence it is on the line. Put T for telling, A for asking or E for exclaiming.

6. I love going to ballet class. ....

7. I almost fell off the stage! ....

8. When are you coming to watch me dance? ....

9. Watch out for the big bug! ....

10. Why do the clouds look white? ....

My score: _____
10

My time: ....
minutes   seconds

Minute 14

Name: .... **Date:** ....

For Questions 1–5, rewrite each sentence correctly on the line.

1. how are you? ....

2. my desk is dirty. ....

3. the clock is black. ....

4. wow, she's tall! ....

5. i play the piano. ....

For Questions 6–10, circle Yes if the sentence ends with the correct punctuation mark or No if it does not.

6. Wow, I just won a new bike.   Yes   No

7. How are Tom and Susie doing.   Yes   No

8. We are taking class pictures on Friday.   Yes   No

9. On what day do we have music class?   Yes   No

10. Scott's birthday is on Saturday?   Yes   No

My score: _____
10

My time: ....
minutes   seconds

Minute 15

Name: .... Date: ....

For Questions 1–6, write each noun in the correct box below.

| bedroom | singer | hospital |
| ring | nurse | brush |

Person	**Place**	**Thing**
1.	3.	5. ....
2.	4.	6. ....

For Questions 7–10, circle the nouns in the sentences.
(**Hint**: Each sentence has two nouns to circle.)

7. The firefighter saved the kitten.

8. There are flowers in the garden.

9. The dog tore up his toy.

10. The nurse took care of my cut.

My score: $\dfrac{}{10}$

My time: ....
minutes   seconds

Minute 16

Name: .... Date: ....

Circle the proper nouns that are missing their capital letters in the sentences below.

1. Mr thomas is my class teacher.

2. I go to bracknell Primary School.

3. Mr Thomas is from cardiff, Wales.

4. He went to the University of bristol.

5. Today our class is going to the london Zoo.

6. johnny's mom is going to help Mr Thomas.

7. Mr greene is going with us as well.

8. We will get to see chi, the famous panda bear.

9. I hope the other panda bear, hua, is there too.

10. My best friend, jennifer, and I can't wait to go!

My score: ─────
10

My time: ....
 minutes   seconds

Verbs 9 8 7 6

Name: .... **Date:** ....

Circle the 10 verbs (action words) in the box below.

chew	dance	jump
pretty	teacher	big
swim	smell	song
puppy	pizza	eraser
clap	walk	drive
red	pillow	hat
computer	paper	kite
type	eat	spider

My score: _____
10

My time: ....
minutes   seconds

Minute 18

Name: .... **Date:** ....

Circle the verb in each sentence.

1. The girl feeds the ducks.

2. The dog barks at the cat.

3. The boys play football.

4. The mother reads a book to her son.

5. I walked around the park.

6. We swam every day in January.

7. The snail slides on the ground.

8. Alex and Jess rode their bikes.

9. The birds chirp in the tree.

10. Jia types on the computer.

My score: $\dfrac{}{10}$

My time: ....
minutes · seconds

Verb tense (present and past)

Name: .... **Date:** ....

Circle the correct verb in each sentence.

1. We (jogs, jogged) in the park yesterday.

2. The boys (play, played) football last night.

3. Mrs Clarke (helps, helped) us every day.

4. Right now I (have, had) long hair.

5. My brother (is, was) at school camp last week.

6. Lisa (dances, danced) in the show two years ago.

7. The baby (cries, cried) all last night.

8. My new dog (licks, licked) me when I have food.

9. The soldier (pulls, pulled) the flag up every morning.

10. The bus driver (chews, chewed) gum all the time.

My score: _____

10

My time: ....

minutes   seconds

Minute 20

Name: .... **Date:** ....

For Questions 1–6, write the correct verb in each sentence.

(**Hint**: When something happens now, it is present tense. When something has happened already, it is past tense.)

Present tense	Past tense
1. The dog .... (scratches scratched) himself.	**2.** I .... my (scratches scratched) itchy arm.
3. I .... when I (yawned yawn) am sleepy.	**4.** She .... all (yawned yawn) morning.
5. We .... with (write wrote) pink pens.	**6.** My friends .... (write wrote) a poem.

For Questions 7–10, circle the correct verb in each sentence.

7. My birthday (is, was) later this month.

8. He (rakes, raked) the leaves yesterday.

9. Sunflowers (look, looked) pretty when they grow tall.

10. Sammy (bowls, bowled) in last week's cricket match.

My score: _____
10

My time: ....
minutes   seconds

Linking verbs (*is, are, am*)

Name: .... **Date:** ....

---

*Circle the correct verb (**is, are, or am**) in each sentence.*

1. My name (is, are, am) Johnny.

2. The leaves (is, are, am) yellow.

3. I (is, are, am) the star of the play.

4. The dog (is, are, am) well trained.

5. My mum (is, are, am) the president of his company.

6. My family (is, are, am) at the hockey match.

7. A lion (is, are, am) a strong animal.

8. I (is, are, am) afraid of the dark.

9. There (is, are, am) five birds in the cage.

10. The flower garden (is, are, am) colourful.

My score: $\dfrac{\quad\quad}{10}$

My time: ....

minutes   seconds

Name: .... **Date:** ....

Circle the correct verb (was or were) in each sentence.

1. The cow (was, were) on the grass.

2. The sun (was, were) so hot, the plants died.

3. The children (was, were) excited about the party.

4. The book (was, were) under the desk.

5. Our costumes (was, were) the best ones.

6. Kathy (was, were) asleep all day!

7. The dolphins (was, were) fun to watch.

8. The cake (was, were) yummy!

9. The streets (was, were) wet from the rain.

10. The spider (was, were) on the window.

My score: _____ / **10**

My time: ....
minutes   seconds

Minute 23

Name: .... **Date:** ....

Circle the correct verb (have, has, or had) in each sentence.

1. We now (have, has, had) three computers in our classroom.

2. The teacher also (have, has, had) her own computer now.

3. Joey and Sam (have, has, had) the same lunch today.

4. Sarah and Huong (have, has, had) a test tomorrow.

5. Our teacher (have, has, had) a little dog.

6. These trees always (have, has, had) lots of leaves.

7. My cousin (have, has, had) a cold right now.

8. We (have, has, had) pizza for lunch yesterday.

9. Rick and Larry (have, has, had) fun last summer.

10. The biscuits I am making (have, has, had) nuts in them.

My score: _____

10

My time: ....

minutes   seconds

Name: ....   **Date:** ....

Circle the adjective (describing word) *in each sentence.*
(**Hint:** Each sentence has one adjective to circle.)

1. The grey puppy licked his paws.

2. The strawberries are sweet.

3. There are five birds in the sky.

4. Kim drew a pretty picture of a rainbow.

5. I tasted the sour lemon.

6. The tiny mouse ran into the hole.

7. My father likes green apples.

8. The loud music hurts my ears.

9. The cat was chased by a mean dog.

10. The little girl's hamster died.

My score: _____   **My time:** ....
             10   minutes   seconds

Minute 25

Name: .... **Date:** ....

Circle the correct adjective in each sentence.

(**Hint**: Adjectives that end in -er compare two things, and adjectives that end in -est compare more than two things.)

1. Mike is (taller, tallest) than Chris.

2. Elaine is the (faster, fastest) painter in art class.

3. Holly is the (slower, slowest) person of all.

4. Flowers are (shorter, shortest) than trees.

5. The sun is (brighter, brightest) than the moon.

6. John is the (smarter, smartest) boy in school.

7. Laura is the (nicer, nicest) girl I know.

8. Cheetahs are (bigger, biggest) than house cats.

9. The plate is (cleaner, cleanest) than the bowl.

10. He dug the (deeper, deepest) hole he could.

My score: $\dfrac{}{10}$ **My time:** ....
minutes   seconds

Name: .... **Date:** ....

For Questions 1–5, insert the missing comma in each address or place.

1. Wendy lives at 43 Combend Road, Exeter Devon.

2. I was born in Newcastle United Kingdom.

3. Last summer, Tony went to Paris France.

4. Her party is at 121 Huston Drive Cork Ireland.

5. My address is 71 Tyne Way Glasgow, Scotland.

For Questions 6–10, insert the missing comma(s) to separate the names from the titles.

6. The US President, Barack Obama left on the plane.

7. The winner of the prize was Jim Tuffin BA (Hons).

8. Mr Wallis CEO of Enterprise Ltd, was early for the meeting.

9. Ms Judy Norton JP was born in Berlin, Germany.

10. Dr JA Sampson Member of the Legislative Assembly liked cats.

My score: _____
10

My time: ....
minutes   seconds

Name: .... Date: ....

For Questions 1–4, insert the missing comma in each sentence.

1. I like to read skate and dance.

2. My brother plays hockey, football rugby and baseball.

3. Sasha ate a hot dog, crisps popcorn and an ice-cream.

4. Kevin saw lions tigers, monkeys and snakes at the zoo.

For Questions 5–10, circle the sentences that use the commas correctly.

5. (a) Carolyn likes, apples oranges and pears.
   (b) Carolyn likes apples, oranges and pears.

6. (a) I went to the beach, the park, and the zoo.
   (b) I went to the beach, the park and the zoo.

7. (a) The teacher gave us scissors glue and crayons.
   (b) The teacher gave us scissors, glue and crayons.

8. (a) We have two birds, a turtle and, a hamster.
   (b) We have two birds, a turtle and a hamster.

9. (a) The flowers are red, yellow and white.
   (b) Our school colours, are red, yellow and white.

10. (a) The farm has, chickens, cows ducks and pigs.
    (b) Thomas has chickens, cows, ducks and pigs.

My score: ___
10

My time: ....
minutes   seconds

Minute 28

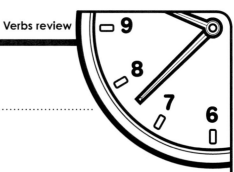

Name: .... **Date:** ....

Read the story and circle the 10 verbs.

Mike's class went on a class excursion to the history museum last

Friday. He saw a large display of dinosaurs and he drew one of the

dinosaurs in his notebook. The teacher told the class to not run or

play in the museum. After the museum tour, the class ate lunch at

the park. After lunch, the class rode back to school on the bus. The

next day, the pupils had to write a story about their trip and read it to

the class.

My score: _____

10

My time: ....
                    minutes   seconds

Name: .... **Date:** ....

For Questions 1–3, write Yes if the underlined word is a verb or No if it is not.

1. Please give this <u>note</u> to your teacher.   ....

2. Simon <u>bumped</u> his head on the wall.   ....

3. My ears hurt from the <u>loud</u> music.   ....

For Questions 4–7, circle Present if the sentence is in the present tense or Past if it is in the past tense.

4. The little boy read 20 books last summer.   Present   Past

5. The children are in the swimming pool.   Present   Past

6. Tom is the class play's lead actor this year.   Present   Past

7. John and Tim were friends in nursery.   Present   Past

For Questions 8–10, circle the correct verb in each sentence.

8. Yesterday (was, were) Dorian's birthday.

9. Martin (is, are, am) on the basketball team.

10. My dog, Lucy, (have, has, had) her puppies last month.

My score: _____
10

My time: ....
     minutes   seconds

Minute 30

Name: .... **Date:** ....

For Questions 1–4, use an adjective from the box to complete each sentence.

red	fresh	fastest	smart

1. Sherry and Mandy are .... pupils.

2. Angela is the .... runner on her team.

3. The shiny .... car had a flat tyre.

4. The mouse found a .... piece of cheese.

For Questions 5–7, circle the adjective in each sentence.

5. The yellow roses grow in the spring.

6. Tonya put roses in her prettiest vase.

7. The roses made a beautiful gift for her mother.

For Questions 8–10, circle the correct adjective in each sentence.

8. Apples are (healthy, healthier, healthiest) than sweets.

9. Regina's poem was the (good, better, best) one of all.

10. A watermelon is much (long, longer, longest) than a banana.

My score: _____ / 10 **My time:** ....
minutes   seconds

Minute 31

Name: .... **Date:** ....

For Questions 1–3, insert the missing comma in each sentence.

1. I like to eat pancakes eggs and bacon for breakfast.

2. My address is 37 Ocean Drive, Poole Dorset.

3. We saw fireworks on New Year's Eve outside the Houses of Parliament London England.

For Questions 4–6, circle the sentences that use the commas correctly.

4. (a) We ate popcorn, nachos and hot dogs at the fair.
   (b) We ate popcorn, nachos and hot dogs, at the fair.

5. (a) In September, 2010 330 people flew into Cadnia South, Australia.
   (b) In September 2010, 330 people flew into Cadnia, South Australia.

6. (a) We live in Shanghai China.
   (b) We live in Shanghai, China.

For Questions 7–10, write Yes if the commas are used correctly or No if they are not.

7. By 1997, 50 people had registered. ....

8. My grandma lives in Belfast, Northern Ireland. ....

9. My favourite fruits are oranges, cherries and grapes. ....

10. His address is 323 Jones Way, Perth Scotland. ....

My score: _____
10

My time: ....
        minutes   seconds

Minute 32 _____

Name: .... **Date:** ....

Circle the correct pronoun in each sentence.

1. (I, Me) love to drink chocolate milk.

2. Is the bus picking (I, me) up for school?

3. The water splashed on (I, me).

4. (I, Me) play the drums in the band.

5. Jamil stands behind (I, me) in line.

6. The two turtles belong to (I, me).

7. (I, Me) visit my grandparents every Sunday.

8. Why do (I, me) have to go to the doctor?

9. The lions and the tigers scare (I, me).

10. The monkeys are looking at (I, me).

My score: _____
10

My time: ....
minutes   seconds

Minute 33

Name: .... **Date:** ....

For Questions 1–5, write Yes if the underlined pronoun is used correctly or No if it is not.

1. <u>Him</u> watches the football match with his dad. ....

2. Dad is getting <u>her</u> a laptop. ....

3. I gave <u>he</u> the directions to my house. ....

4. <u>Him</u> had the flu for two weeks! ....

5. <u>She</u> makes dinner every night. ....

For Questions 6–10, circle the pronoun that could take the place of the underlined noun.

6. <u>Harold</u> has three bikes in his shed. He Him

7. <u>Maria</u> likes the colour pink. She Her

8. Tom plays tennis with <u>Meg</u>. she her

9. The teacher asked <u>Doug</u> for the answer. he him

10. <u>Kelly</u> caught more fish at the lake. She Her

My score: _____
10

My time: ....
minutes seconds

Minute 34

9
8
7   **6**

Name: .... Date: ....

Circle the correct pronoun in each sentence.

1. (We, Us) are going to the pet shop.

2. My best friend is going with (we, us).

3. (We, Us) can get a hamster at the pet shop.

4. I hope that the hamster likes (we, us).

5. (We, Us) are going to name him Harvey.

6. (We, Us) stay up late at the weekends.

7. Our mother tells (we, us) to do our homework.

8. Sometimes (we, us) eat cake and ice-cream for dessert.

9. (We, Us) always brush our teeth after dinner.

10. My dad reads (we, us) a bedtime story every night.

My score: _____

10

My time: ....

minutes   seconds

Minute 35

Name: .... **Date:** ....

For Questions 1–5, write the pronoun they or them on the line to take the place of the underlined words in each sentence.
(**Hint**: Remember that a sentence must begin with a capital letter.)

1. The turtles like to eat lettuce.   ....

2. We are waiting for Helen and Jen.   ....

3. The Kesslers are moving to Margaret River.   ....

4. Sam and Jason are going with us to the beach.   ....

5. Do we have to take Sue and Jon with us?   ....

For Questions 6–10, write Yes if the underlined pronoun is used correctly or No if it is not.

6. <u>Them</u> are both my best friends.   ....

7. We should invite <u>them</u> to play hide-and-seek. ....

8. My parents were happy when <u>they</u> saw my marks. ....

9. The sweets are so good, I could eat <u>them</u> all! ....

10. <u>Them</u> are the best dancers in the show.   ....

My score: ───
10

My time: ....
minutes   seconds

Minute 36

Name: ....   **Date:** ....

For Questions 1–6, circle the noun that is plural in each sentence.
(**Hint**: Plural means more than one.)

1. My sister does not like to wear dresses.

2. Spot chases the cats in the neighbourhood.

3. The two girls always play with the ball at break.

4. I went to many beaches this summer.

5. The foxes ran quickly around the paddock.

6. The ponies were fun to ride.

For Questions 7–10, circle the correct plural noun in each sentence.

7. I have two best (friends, friendes) at school.

8. Susie got lots of (toys, toies) for her birthday.

9. Tony and his (brotheres, brothers) like football.

10. Spain has many (cities, citys) by the beach.

My score: ———
10

My time: ....
minutes   seconds

Minute 37

Name: ....

Date: ....

For Questions 1–5, circle the plural noun that is spelt correctly in each pair.

1. ponies   ponys

2. babys   babies

3. truckies   trucks

4. foxes   foxs

5. glassies   glasses

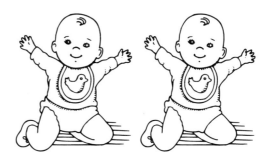

For Questions 6–10, write each noun in plural form.
(**Hint**: Add -s or -es to the end of each noun.)

6. pencil   ....

7. apple   ....

8. box   ....

9. boy   ....

10. class   ....

My score: _____
10

My time: ....
minutes   seconds

Minute 38

Name: .... Date: ....

For Questions 1–5, add an apostrophe and s ('s) to the underlined nouns to make them possessive.
(**Hint**: Possessive nouns show ownership by a person, place or thing.)

1. The <u>baby</u> rattle was on the floor. ....

2. <u>Nicole</u> dress is pink and white. ....

3. The <u>painter</u> lunchbreak is now. ....

4. The <u>clock</u> battery stopped working. ....

5. The <u>city</u> lights are bright at night. ....

For Questions 6–8, circle the correct possessive form that matches each group of italiced words.

6. *neck of a giraffe:*   a neck's giraffe   a giraffe's neck

7. *mat that belongs to the dog:*   the dog's mat   the mat's dog

8. *shell of the turtle:*   the turtle's shell   the shell's turtle

For Questions 9–10, rewrite each group of words to make them possessive.

9. tyres of the car ....

10. dress that belongs to Ming ....

My score: ____
10

My time: ....
minutes   seconds

Minute 39

Name: .... **Date:** ....

For Questions 1–5, circle the contraction in each sentence.

1. Don't walk in the middle of the street!

2. I'm going to the pet shop to buy a turtle.

3. The little boy can't reach the biscuit jar.

4. I haven't read that book yet.

5. We shouldn't be mean to the new pupil.

For Questions 6–10, write Yes if the contraction is spelt correctly or No if it is not.

6. was'nt ....

7. he's ....

8. couldn' ....

9. it's ....

10. I'm ....

My score: **My time:**

10 ....

minutes   seconds

Minute 40

Name: .... **Date:** ....

For Questions 1–5, write the contractions for the underlined words.

1. I <u>have not</u> finished my homework.   ....

2. The puppy <u>was not</u> scared of the big dog.   ....

3. <u>She is</u> very happy to see you.   ....

4. <u>I will</u> buy a pencil at school.   ....

5. I <u>did not</u> finish the maths test.   ....

For Questions 6–10, circle the correct two words that make up each contraction in italics.

6. *can't:*	can not	could not
7. *isn't:*	am not	is not
8. *don't:*	did not	do not
9. *hasn't:*	has not	have not
10. *shouldn't:*	shall not	should not

My score: _____
10

My time: ....
minutes   seconds

Minute 41

Name: ....   Date: ....

For Questions 1–4, use the two words to make a
compound word.

1. dog   house   ....

2. coat   rain   ....

3. sun   glasses   ....

4. paper   news   ....

For Questions 5–10, make compound words using the words in the
box below. Use each word only once.

5. ....

6. ....

7. ....

8. ....

9. ....

10. ....

after	noon
tooth	home
melon	sea
father	water
paste	grand
horse	work

My score: _____
                 10

My time: ....
              minutes   seconds

Name: .... Date: ....

For Questions 1–4, circle the compound word in each sentence.

1. The twins play in the backyard.

2. Please go outside and wash the dog.

3. We are riding our bikes to the playground.

4. Eric and Tony play basketball on the same team.

For Questions 5–10, write Yes if the word is a compound word or No if it is not.

5. sunshine   ....

6. television   ....

7. calendar   ....

8. upstairs   ....

9. background   ....

10. computer   ....

My score: $\dfrac{\quad}{10}$

My time: ....
                              minutes   seconds

Name: .... Date: ....

For Questions 1–5, replace the underlined noun or nouns with a pronoun.

1. <u>Karen</u> missed school all week.   ....

2. <u>Dan and Jim</u> went to the cinema.   ....

3. Mike gave <u>Mark</u> a birthday card.   ....

4. <u>Bob</u> broke his computer again.   ....

5. <u>Dorothy</u> can speak Japanese very well.   ....

For Questions 6–10, circle the correct pronoun in each sentence.

6. Our teacher played cricket with (we, us) today.

7. (He, Him) wants to become a doctor.

8. (They, Them) are having a party next Saturday.

9. Marcy didn't tell (she, her) the truth.

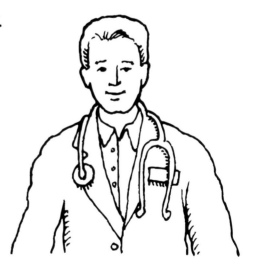

10. (I, Me) can meet you at the library later.

My score: _____
10

My time: ....
minutes   seconds

Minute 44

Name: ....   **Date:** ....

For Questions 1–5, write the nouns in plural form.

1. carrot   ....

2. family   ....

3. couch   ....

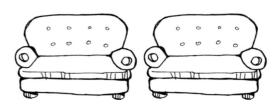

4. class   ....

5. axe   ....

For Questions 6–10, circle the possessive noun in each sentence.

6. My (dog's, dogs) tail wags fast.

7. The (cakes, cake's) frosting is vanilla flavoured.

8. The (children, children's) bikes are in the garage.

9. That (chair's, chairs) leg is broken.

10. His (computers, computer's) screen is dirty.

My score: $\dfrac{\quad\quad}{10}$

My time: ....
 minutes   seconds

Minute 45

Name: .... Date: ....

For Questions 1–5, write the contraction for the two words.

1. he is   ....

2. does not   ....

3. are not   ....

4. you are   ....

5. you will   ....

For Questions 6–10, write the two words that make up each contraction.

6. would've   ....

7. won't   ....

8. isn't   ....

9. didn't   ....

10. mustn't   ....

My score: _____ / **10**

My time: ....
minutes   seconds

Minute 46

Name: .... **Date:** ....

Circle the compound word in each sentence.

1. We saw skyscrapers in New York City.

2. The earthworm crawled through the dirt.

3. Do you have any peppermints?

4. We built a snowman after the storm.

5. My wristwatch stopped working.

6. The sunflowers grew as tall as I am.

7. My dad built a birdhouse for my garden.

8. Julie sent me a postcard from her holiday location.

9. Jake was scared of the rattlesnake at the zoo.

10. Katie forgot to do her homework.

My score: _____
10

My time: ....
minutes   seconds

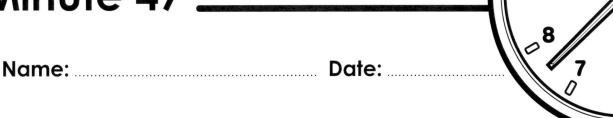

Name: .... **Date:** ....

For Questions 1–6, write the best synonym for each word.
(**Hint**: A synonym is a word that means the same thing or almost the same thing.)

| beautiful | small | scream | angry | sleepy | hop |

1. mad   ....

2. yell   ....

3. pretty   ....

4. skip   ....

5. tired   ....

6. tiny   ....

For Questions 7–10, circle the synonym for each underlined word.

7. Angel <u>dislikes</u> cats.   hates   loves

8. My <u>friend</u> George is funny.   buddy   girl

9. Tosha was <u>sad</u> when her fish died.   happy   unhappy

10. I've <u>finished</u> my homework already.   completed   started

My score: _____
10

My time: ....
                    minutes   seconds

Minute 48

Name: .... **Date:** ....

For Questions 1–4, circle the two synonyms in each group of words.

1. quiet   noisy   silent   bark

2. old   new   ancient   dull

3. yell   talk   speak   walk

4. rich   poor   wealthy   nice

For Questions 5–10, write Yes if the pairs of words are synonyms or No if they are not.

5. run   walk   ....

6. cook   eat   ....

7. cry   smile   ....

8. sleep   awake   ....

9. jump   hop   ....

10. draw   illustrate   ....

My score: $\frac{}{10}$

My time: ....
               minutes   seconds

Prim-Ed Publishing®   www.prim-ed.com

Minute 49

Name: .... **Date:** ....

For Questions 1–6, write the best antonym for each word.
(**Hint**: An antonym is a word that means the opposite of something.)

| sit | asleep | forget | up | run | go |

1. stop ....

2. down ....

3. stand ....

4. awake ....

5. remember ....

6. walk ....

For Questions 7–10, circle the antonym for each underlined word.

7. The diamond ring is <u>shiny</u>.   dull   bright

8. The music was <u>noisy</u>.   loud   quiet

9. The <u>little</u> dog ran to his owner.   huge   tiny

10. My mother said to clean my
    <u>dirty</u> room.   neat   filthy

My score: _____
10

My time: ....
                    minutes   seconds

Minute 50

Name: .... **Date:** ....

For Questions 1–6, circle the antonym for each word in italics.

1. *early:*   on time   late

2. *cold:*   frozen   hot

3. *left:*   right   wrong

4. *good:*   super   terrible

5. *wet:*   dry   damp

6. *ugly:*   pretty   strong

For Questions 7–10, complete each sentence with an antonym for the underlined word.

7. The swing went <u>up</u> and ....

8. My brother is a <u>slow</u> runner, but I am a .... runner.

9. I don't like <u>big</u> dogs. I like .... dogs.

10. The bird flew <u>high</u> in the sky, then .... to the ground.

My score: $\dfrac{\quad\quad}{10}$ **My time:** ....
                                   minutes   seconds

Minute 51

Name: ....   Date: ....

For Questions 1–6, circle the correct homophone in each sentence.
(**Hint**: Homophones are words that sound the same but are spelt differently and have different meanings.)

1. The (sun, son) is shining brightly in the sky.

2. We can (see, sea) the top of the mountain from here.

3. May I please have a (piece, peace) of cake?

4. The hawk watches his (prey, pray) from the tree.

5. A (be, bee) in my garden stung me on my arm.

6. My favourite colour is sky (blew, blue).

For Questions 7–10, write Yes if the words are homophones or No if they are not.

7. right   write   ....

8. dig   bury   ....

9. to   too   ....

10. small   little   ....

My score: ____
10

My time: ....
                      minutes   seconds

Minute 52

Name: .... Date: ....

For Questions 1–6, circle the correct meaning for the underlined homograph in each sentence.

(**Hint**: Homographs are words that are spelt the same—and *sometimes* sound the same—but have different meanings.)

1. Be careful not to <u>break</u> anything!
   - (a) a rest
   - (b) to smash

2. He hit the ball hard with the <u>bat</u>.
   - (a) a piece of wood or metal
   - (b) a flying mammal

3. The <u>wind</u> blew my hat off.
   - (a) to turn
   - (b) a strong current of air

4. The <u>bug</u> crawled up his leg.
   - (a) to bother
   - (b) an insect

5. Don't <u>tear</u> the paper.
   - (a) a drop of liquid from eye
   - (b) to rip

6. You should never <u>lie</u> to your parents.
   - (a) to rest down flat
   - (b) to speak untruthfully

For Questions 7–10, draw a line to match the underlined homograph in each sentence with its correct meaning.

7. Please <u>bow</u> when the Queen walks in.

8. She had a beautiful <u>bow</u> in her hair.

9. I will <u>plant</u> some roses today.

10. The <u>plant</u> grew very tall.

(a) a living thing with leaves

(b) to put something in the ground

(c) to bend down from the waist

(d) a knotted ribbon

My score: _____ / 10

My time: ....
            minutes   seconds

Minute 53

Name: .... **Date:** ....

*For Questions 1–5, add the prefix re- or un- to the
beginning of the underlined word in each sentence.*

Use the information in the box about prefixes to help you.

(**Hint**: A prefix changes the meaning of a word by adding a group of letters to the
beginning of a word.)

Prefix	Meaning	Example
re- un-	again; back not; opposite	<u>re</u>do (do again) <u>un</u>clean (not clean)

1. Yesterday Mrs Chen was <u>happy</u>, but today she is ....

2. I <u>write</u> my homework quickly and then I .... it.

3. Don't eat an .... snack if you could eat a <u>healthy</u> one instead.

4. <u>Fill</u> the glasses with water and be sure to .... them when they get empty.

5. I was really <u>lucky</u> today, but I was .... yesterday.

*For Questions 6–10, draw a line to match the underlined word in each
sentence with its correct definition.*

6. Her birthday gifts are still <u>unwrapped</u>.

7. My dress was still dirty, so I <u>rewashed</u> it.

8. The directions for the test were <u>unclear</u>.

9. Please <u>redraw</u> that messy illustration.

10. Susie <u>rewrapped</u> the gifts after she peeked at them.

(a) not clear

(b) wrapped again

(c) not wrapped

(d) washed again

(e) draw again

My score: _____
10

My time: ....
minutes   seconds

Minute 54

Name: .... **Date:** ....

For Questions 1–5, use the information in the box about suffixes to write the word that best completes each sentence.

(**Hint:** A suffix changes the meaning of a word by adding a group of letters to the end of a word.)

Suffix	Meaning	Example
-er -ful	one who; a person who full of	sing<u>er</u> (a person who sings) pain<u>ful</u> (full of pain)

1. The teacher said that Johnny is a good ....
   (**helpful   helper**)

2. Michelle's mean words were .... to me.
   (**hurter   hurtful**)

3. Tonya is the best .... on their team.
   (**playful   player**)

4. The teacher thinks Holly is a .... pupil.
   (**helpful   helper**)

5. The monkeys at the zoo are .... all day.
   (**playful   player**)

For Questions 6–10, underline the word that ends with a suffix in each sentence, and write its meaning on the line.

6. Jasmine was a famous painter.   ....

7. The walls are bright and colourful.   ....

8. Everyone was cheerful at the party.   ....

9. Omar wants to be a teacher.   ....

10. Ben is hopeful about his grades.   ....

My score: _____
10

My time: ....
minutes   seconds

Name: .... **Date:** ....

For Questions 1–6, write the words in the box in alphabetical order.

| duck | skate | weather | job | five | grapes |

1. ....

2. ....

3. ....

4. ....

5. ....

6. ....

For Questions 7–10, write Yes if the groups of words are in alphabetical order or No if they are not.

7. king   prince   queen   ....

8. book   library   magazine   ....

9. sing   dance   act   ....

10. black   brown   red   ....

My score: ____
10

My time: ....
                         minutes   seconds

Minute 56

Name: .... **Date:** ....

For Questions 1–4, write each set of words in alphabetical order.

1. snap, shake, slide ....

2. apple, any, already ....

3. grape, great, grew ....

4. drum, drink, draw ....

For Questions 5–10, write the words in the box in alphabetical order.

house	heat	head	home	hum	handsome

5. ....

6. ....

7. ....

8. ....

9. ....

10. ....

My score: $\dfrac{\rule{2cm}{0.4pt}}{10}$ **My time:** ....
                                                        minutes   seconds

Minute 57

Name: ....   **Date:** ....

Write S if the pairs of words are synonyms (mean the same thing) or A if they are antonyms (mean the opposite).

1. neat   clean   ....

2. ugly   pretty   ....

3. high   low   ....

4. lost   missing   ....

5. good   bad   ....

6. happy   cheerful   ....

7. sick   well   ....

8. large   huge   ....

9. hard   easy   ....

10. nice   sweet   ....

My score: _____   **My time:** ....
$$\overline{10}$$
minutes   seconds

Minute 58

Name: .... Date: ....

For Questions 1–6, write a homophone for each word.
(**Hint**: Remember that homophones are words that sound the same but are spelt differently and have different meanings.)

1. son   ....

2. maid   ....

3. plain   ....

4. meat   ....

5. right   ....

6. knew   ....

For Questions 7–10, draw a line to match the underlined homograph in each sentence with its correct meaning.
(**Hint**: Remember that homographs are words that are spelt the same—and sometimes sound the same—but have different meanings.)

7. That <u>duck</u> quacks all day and night!

(a) to bend down quickly

8. He had to <u>duck</u> so the ball didn't hit him.

(b) a built-in bowl with faucets

9. The heavy rock will <u>sink</u> in the water.

(c) a waterbird with a wide beak

10. Our kitchen <u>sink</u> is full of dishes.

(d) to go down below

My score: ____ / 10

My time: ....
minutes   seconds

Name: .... **Date:** ....

For Questions 1–5, write P if the underlined word begins with a prefix or S if it ends with a suffix.

1. The old glue stick was so dry, it was <u>useless</u>. ....

2. Please <u>reorder</u> more paper for the office. ....

3. I am so <u>thankful</u> for all of your help! ....

4. Charlie banged on our door very <u>loudly</u>. ....

5. Do not <u>unlock</u> the door for a stranger. ....

For Questions 6–10, use a word from the box to complete each sentence.

unpack	driver	reread	beautiful	replay

6. When the video game ends, I .... it from the beginning.

7. It is dangerous to be a race car ....

8. We .... our clothes in the hotel room.

9. The rainbow in the sky was ....

10. I have to .... the answer I got wrong.

My score: ____
10

My time: ....
minutes   seconds

Minute 60

Name: .... **Date:** ....

Write Yes if the words are in alphabetical order or
No if they are not.

1. sofa, table, chair ....

2. dirt, rock, water ....

3. bowl, cup, plate ....

4. bear, monkey, lion ....

5. cereal, fruit, meat ....

6. water, milk, juice ....

7. bush, flower, plants ....

8. cook, doctor, nurse ....

9. rest, socks, shoes ....

10. cloud, moon, star ....

My score: _____
10

My time: ....
minutes   seconds

Minute 61

Name: .... **Date:** ....

For Questions 1–4, circle the correct article (a or an) in each sentence.

(**Hint**: Use *a* before words that begin with a consonant sound, and use *an* before words that begin with a vowel sound.)

1. I have (a, an) ant farm at home.

2. Our school has (a, an) big library.

3. I am getting (a, an) new pair of shoes.

4. (A, An) apple is a healthy snack.

For Questions 5–10, write the correct article (a or an) that goes before each word.

5. .... telephone

6. .... man

7. .... egg

8. .... nose

9. .... iron

10. .... teacher

My score: _____
$\dfrac{}{10}$

My time: ....
minutes   seconds

Minute 62

Name: .... **Date:** ....

Complete each sentence with the missing article: a, an, or the.

(**Hint**: Use *the* before a word that stands for a specific person, place or thing. You can use *the* before a word that begins with a consonant or a vowel.)

1. My class is going to .... Dublin Zoo this year.

2. I won .... prize at the cricket competition.

3. .... older pupils put on a play.

4. I want .... ice-cream.

5. Our teacher took .... picture of us at the zoo.

6. She is .... smartest pupil in class.

7. I got .... new bike for my birthday.

8. We went to .... dentist for a checkup.

9. Have you met .... new neighbours?

10. .... orange tastes better than an apple.

My score: ———
10

My time: ....
minutes   seconds

Minute 63

Name: .... **Date:** ....

For Questions 1–4, circle the correct past-tense verb in each sentence.
(**Hint**: Past tense means that something has happened already.)

1. I (feeded, fed) my dog twice yesterday.

2. Marcus (throwed, threw) the ball to his father.

3. The children (writed, wrote) a class play.

4. We (maked, made) biscuits for the club's cake sale.

For Questions 5–10, circle the correct past-tense form of each italic verb.

5. *take:*   took   taked

6. *run:*   runned   ran

7. *freeze:*   freezed   froze

8. *stand:*   stood   standed

9. *leave:*   leaved   left

10. *read:*   readed   read

My score: $\dfrac{}{10}$

My time: ....
                minutes   seconds

Minute 64

Name: .... **Date:** ....

For Questions 1–6, write each verb from the box next to its correct past-tense form.

fight	hold	take	wear	run	catch

1. held ....

2. took ....

3. caught ....

4. fought ....

5. wore ....

6. ran ....

For Questions 7–10, circle the correct verb in each sentence.

7. My mother (taked, took) the dog to the vet.

8. The flowers (growed, grew) in September.

9. The children (swimmed, swam) in the pool all summer.

10. I (selled, sold) hotdogs last Saturday.

My score: ___
10

My time: ....
minutes   seconds

Minute 65

Name: .... **Date:** ....

For Questions 1–6, circle the correct plural form of each noun in italics.

1. *calf:*   calfs   calves

2. *man:*   men   mans

3. *woman:*   womans   women

4. *mouse:*   mice   mouses

5. *loaf:*   loafs   loaves

6. *knife:*   knives   knifes

For Questions 7–10, circle the correct plural noun in each sentence.

7. The (childs, children) walk to the shop.

8. The (leafs, leaves) fell from the tree.

9. My (foots, feet) were hurting after I ran.

10. The horse's (hoofs, hooves) were sore after the race.

My score: _____
10

My time: ....
                     minutes   seconds

Minute 66

9 8 7 6

Name: .... **Date:** ....

For Questions 1–5, circle the plural noun in each sentence.

1. The geese flew over our house.

2. There were a lot of people at the cricket match.

3. I have two shelves on my bedroom wall.

4. Be careful because the knives are very sharp!

5. We baked two loaves of bread for dinner.

For Questions 6–10, write the correct plural form for the underlined noun in each sentence.

6. I lost two <u>tooth</u> last week.   ....

7. The three <u>man</u> built a fence.   ....

8. The <u>child</u> took a trip with their parents.   ....

9. Why are so many <u>person</u> here?   ....

10. All the <u>leaf</u> are red, yellow and orange.   ....

My score: $\frac{}{10}$ **My time:** ....
                                                     minutes   seconds

Name: ....   **Date:** ....

Answer the questions about how, when or where something happens.

1. The deer quickly crossed the street.
   How did the deer cross the street?   ....

2. The little girl ate her food fast.
   How did the little girl eat her food?   ....

3. They found your house easily.
   How did they find your house?   ....

4. We will go camping tomorrow.
   When will we go camping?   ....

5. The Jones family went to the beach on
   Saturday.
   When did the Jones family go to the beach? ....

6. My father and I flew our kites yesterday.
   When did my father and I fly our kites?   ....

7. The accident was near my house.
   Where was the accident?   ....

8. The dog slept outside.
   Where did the dog sleep?   ....

9. The aeroplane flew above our house.
   Where did the plane fly?   ....

10. The cat's toy rolled under the table.
    Where did the cat's toy roll?   ....

My score: _____
10

My time: ....
                minutes   seconds

Minute 68

Name: .... **Date:** ....

For Questions 1–6, use the adverbs in the box to complete the sentences below. Use each adverb only once.
(**Hint**: An adverb is a word that describes a verb and tells how, when, or where something happens.)

quickly	carefully	slowly	sadly	safely	neatly

1. The snail .... crawled on the grass.

2. I .... made up my bed.

3. We were .... inside during the storm.

4. Jill drove .... in the hail.

5. I .... got ready for school this morning.

6. Kelly spoke .... about her cat that died.

For Questions 7–10, write whether the underlined adverb tells how, when or where something happens in each sentence.

7. Kate and Sofia are going skating <u>tonight</u>. ....

8. George <u>sadly</u> cried when he lost the game. ....

9. Monica whispered <u>softly</u> into the telephone. ....

10. The cat played <u>inside</u> the house. ....

My score: $\frac{\quad\quad}{10}$ **My time:** ....
.... minutes   seconds

www.prim-ed.com   Prim-Ed Publishing®

Name: .... **Date:** ....

For Questions 1–6, circle the correct verb in each sentence.

1. Barry (brush, brushes) his teeth three times a day.

2. Dee (ate, eats) a sandwich for lunch yesterday.

3. The library (open, opens) at noon on Saturday.

4. Maxine (rides, rode) her bike this morning.

5. The puppy (scratched, scratch) behind his ears.

6. I (wrote, writed) a poem for the talent show.

For Questions 7–10, circle the correct noun in each sentence.

7. The three (boys, boy) are best friends.

8. An (apples, apple) is on the teacher's desk.

9. The (flower, flowers) smell sweet and fresh.

10. The (children, child) play after school.

My score: _____

10

My time: ....
minutes   seconds

Minute 70

Name: .... Date: ....

For Questions 1–5, write Yes if the sentence is written correctly or No if it is not.

(**Hint**: The verb of the sentence must agree with the subject noun in number; for example: *One* girl goes to the shop, *two* girls go to the shop.)

1. Anthony go fishing with his dad. ....

2. Sue listens to the birds chirp. ....

3. The mouse run from the cat. ....

4. The bookstore is closed. ....

5. Bianca eat a snack in the afternoon. ....

For Questions 6–10, circle the correct noun and verb in each sentence.

6. The six (child, children) (play, plays) football.

7. A (chair, chairs) (fall, fell) on the floor.

8. The two (lady, ladies) (walk, walks) their dogs.

9. Please (wash, washes) all the (plates, plate).

10. The three (kid, kids) (helps, helped) their dad.

My score: $\dfrac{}{10}$ **My time:** ....
minutes   seconds

Name: .... **Date:** ....

Write Yes *if the underlined article is used correctly or* No *if it is not.*

1. <u>The</u> man climbed the tall mountain.   ....

2. <u>An</u> frog jumped into the pond.   ....

3. My dad's computer has <u>a</u> old keyboard.   ....

4. Charlie is <u>a</u> only pupil who is absent.   ....

5. Jenna is eating <u>a</u> orange.   ....

6. Chloe chose <u>the</u> red dress, not the blue one.   ....

7. We had a picnic at <u>an</u> park.   ....

8. Jane is <u>a</u> friend of mine.   ....

9. Lana had fun on <u>the</u> swings.   ....

10. I ate <u>a</u> egg sandwich for breakfast.   ....

My score: $\dfrac{}{10}$ **My time:** ....
                                                            minutes   seconds

Minute 72

Name: .... Date: ....

For Questions 1–5, circle the correct verb to complete each sentence.

1. I (tore, tear) a hole in my favourite skirt.

2. Mandy (thinked, thought) she had another book to read.

3. Jasmine and her sister (swimmed, swam) in their pool.

4. Kel (freezed, froze) the water bottles.

5. The birds (flied, flew) to their new nest.

For Questions 6–10, write the correct plural form for each noun.

6. mouse ....

7. foot ....

8. wolf ....

9. fish ....

10. deer ....

My score: _____
10

My time: ....
minutes   seconds

Name: .... **Date:** ....

Circle the adverbs in the sentences below.
(**Hint**: Remember that adverbs tell how, when or where something happens.)

1. The dog lazily walked into his kennel.

2. May we go anywhere we want?

3. The music shop moved closer to my house.

4. We made it safely to New York.

5. The cat drinks milk every day.

6. Carrie sat across from Hai.

7. Marcia softly brushed the dog's fur.

8. He angrily told me no!

9. The girl neatly wrote the alphabet.

10. Sara can easily win the singing contest.

My score: _____
10

My time: ....
minutes   seconds

Minute 74

Name: .... **Date:** ....

Write Yes *if the sentences are written correctly or* No *if they are not.*
(**Hint**: Remember that the verb of the sentence must agree with the subject noun in number; for example: *One* girl *goes* to the shop, *two girls* go *to the shop.*)

1. The growling dog scare me. ....

2. My cat love to climb big trees. ....

3. I swim in my neighbour's pool. ....

4. The basket were too small for my flowers. ....

5. They ride their bikes on the beach. ....

6. I smells the paint in the room. ....

7. The sour lemon tastes terrible. ....

8. Michael are going to the dentist tomorrow. ....

9. John run with his dad on the track. ....

10. Today is a perfect day to go swimming. ....

My score: _____ / **10**   **My time:** ....

minutes   seconds

Minute 75

Name: .... Date: ....

For Questions 1–4, write C if the sentence is complete or I if it is incomplete.

1. I eat a snack when I get home from school. ....

2. My favourite food. ....

3. Make sure to brush your teeth after each meal. ....

4. The sleeping dog. ....

For Questions 5–7, write Yes if the sentences are in the correct word order or No if they are not.

5. Becky garden in the played. ....

6. Went to the aquarium our class. ....

7. We are going to the cinema. ....

For Questions 8–10, circle the sentences that are written correctly.

8. (a) officer george came to the school to speak.
   (b) Officer George came to the school to speak.

9. (a) Edwina's mum is from Kuala Lumpur, Malaysia.
   (b) Edwina's mum is from Kuala lumpur, Malaysia.

10. (a) Dr Jones is the teacher at longwood Primary.
    (b) Dr Jones is a teacher at Longwood Primary.

My score: _____
10

My time: ....
minutes   seconds

Minute 76

Name: .... **Date:** ....

Circle the words or groups of words that should begin with capital letters.

(**Hint**: There are two words or groups of words in each sentence to circle.)

1. jamie attends melville Primary.

2. her teacher's name is ms rice.

3. cindy and marcia are Jan's best friends.

4. we had fun this summer at ocean world.

5. my sister and i climbed the tall staircase.

6. my brother, kyle, likes the water slides.

7. next year, my parents are taking us to luna park.

8. our house on butler road was sold.

9. my birthday is next tuesday.

10. mr turner picked allen to be the group leader.

My score: _____
10

My time: ....
minutes   seconds

Name: ....   **Date:** ....

For Questions 1–5, add the correct end punctuation mark to each sentence.

1. What does this say ....

2. I had to clean my room before I could play ....

3. May we go to the beach today ....

4. Mrs Todd taught a lesson on weather today ....

5. Don't ever do that again ....

*For Questions 6–10, read each sentence and write the type of sentence it is on the line. Put **T** for telling, **A** for asking or **E** for exclaiming.*

6. How many apples are in the basket?   ....

7. I just won a new bicycle!   ....

8. My dad works at the post office.   ....

9. May we have one more minute to finish?   ....

10. The plane crashed into the mountain!   ....

My score: _____ / **10**

My time: ....
minutes   seconds

Apply your grammar knowledge

Name: .... Date: ....

Circle two nouns and underline one verb in each sentence.

1. The firefighter saved the cat from the burning house.

2. The flowers need a lot of water and sunlight.

3. The toy got full of mud in the garden.

4. The nurse put a bandage on my cut.

5. Greg washes his dog in the bath.

6. Tony sprays water on his sister.

7. The child ran out of the car and into the street.

8. My friends played games after school.

9. Susie reads a lot of books during the holidays.

10. My teacher marked my test this morning.

My score: _____
10

My time: ....
minutes   seconds

www.prim-ed.com   Prim-Ed Publishing®

Minute 79

Name: .... **Date:** ....

For Questions 1–4, write the nouns in plural form.

1. girl   ....

2. ditch   ....

3. baby   ....

4. mouse   ....

For Questions 5–10, circle the correct plural noun in each sentence.

5. There are five school (buses, busies) in the car park.

6. I have three older (sisteres, sisters).

7. Our dog had seven (puppys, puppies).

8. We took swimming (classies, classes) this summer.

9. Yasmine takes her (boxs, boxes) of books to the car.

10. The (floweres, flowers) in Mrs Paul's garden are now blooming.

My score: _____ / **10**

My time: ....
                 minutes   seconds

Minute 80

Name: .... Date: ....

For Questions 1–4, circle Present if the sentence is in the present tense or Past if it is in the past tense.

1. Serena gave Donna tennis lessons this morning.   Present   Past

2. James brought the sandwiches to the picnic.   Present   Past

3. The birds are in the sky.   Present   Past

4. We are celebrating Kath's birthday.   Present   Past

For Questions 5–10, write Yes if the sentence has the correct verb tense or No if it does not.

5. We jump in the pool yesterday.   ....

6. The cats played on the table now.   ....

7. I helped my mother clean the house last week.   ....

8. She bump her elbow yesterday on the wall.   ....

9. I learned how to count to 100 last year.   ....

10. The turtle eats a fish ten minutes ago.   ....

My score: _____   My time: ....
10   minutes   seconds

Apply your grammar knowledge

Name: ....   Date: ....

For Questions 1–3, circle the adjective in each sentence.

1. I gave my mum orange tulips for Mother's Day.

2. The sad puppy was looking for a home.

3. The strong man saved us.

For Questions 4–10, use the adjectives in the box to complete each sentence. Use each adjective only once.

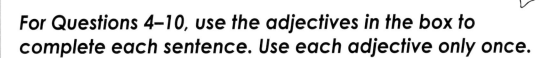

| bitter | sour | sweet | spicy | fresh | handsome | purple |

4. The chocolate cake was too ....

5. I don't like lemons because they taste ....

6. The .... apple was not very good.

7. I burned my mouth eating the .... chicken wings.

8. I think .... grapes taste better than green grapes.

9. We bought .... fruits and vegetables at the market.

10. The .... man over there is my husband.

My score: $\frac{\qquad}{10}$

My time: ....
minutes   seconds

Name: .... **Date:** ....

For Questions 1–5, write Yes if the underlined verb is used correctly or No if it is not.

1. We <u>was</u> at school during the snowstorm. ....

2. The dog <u>is</u> scared of the water. ....

3. Nick <u>have</u> five stickers in his album. ....

4. They <u>am</u> my cousins from Italy. ....

5. The excursion <u>is</u> tomorrow afternoon. ....

For Questions 6–10, circle the correct verb in each sentence.

6. I (is, am) the Pupil of the Month for April.

7. Maths (is, are) one of my favourite subjects.

8. Mrs Gomez (has, have) 16 pupils in her class.

9. The horses (was, were) so gentle and beautiful.

10. Becky and I (is, are) both in karate classes.

My score: _____ **My time:** ....
 $\dfrac{}{10}$ minutes seconds

Minute 83

Name: .... **Date:** ....

For Questions 1–5, write Yes if the commas are used correctly or No if they are not.

1. We will need glue, crayons and scissors. ....

2. Marie got, clothes, a watch and shoes. ....

3. Amy's wedding will be in Paris, France. ....

4. We live at 92, Lombard Street, Leeds. ....

5. Let's, eat Grandma. ....

For Questions 6–10, circle the sentences that are written correctly.

6. (a) Brian, Mike and Chris are in a rock band.
   (b) Brian, Mike and, Chris are in a rock band.

7. (a) My mother was born in Slough, Berkshire, England.
   (b) My mother was born in, Slough, Berkshire, England.

8. (a) We are going to Toulouse, France, this summer.
   (b) We are going to Toulouse France this summer.

9. (a) My address is 37 Hunter Way, Birmingham.
   (b) My address is 37 Hunter Way Birmingham.

10. (a) I ate a hamburger, hot chips and, an apple for lunch.
    (b) I ate a hamburger, hot chips and an apple for lunch.

My score: $\dfrac{}{10}$

My time: ....
minutes seconds

Minute 84

Name: .... Date: ....

Write Yes *if the underlined pronoun in each sentence is correct or* No *if it is not.*

1. <u>Her</u> made Thai beef salad and potatoes for us. ....

2. <u>Me</u> am not going to the cinema with them. ....

3. Justin is mad because you told <u>him</u> to leave. ....

4. <u>They</u> went to Canada to visit their family. ....

5. Why does the puppy always follow <u>us</u>? ....

6. I will ask the teacher when I see <u>she</u>. ....

7. Mom and Dad will be happy if you help <u>they</u>. ....

8. Jessica's sister wants to play with <u>her</u>. ....

9. <u>We</u> only have one hour left in the library. ....

10. <u>I</u> am shopping for his birthday present today. ....

My score: _____
10

My time: ....
minutes   seconds

Minute 85

Name: .... **Date:** ....

For Questions 1–5, write the words that make up each contraction.

1. shouldn't ....

2. don't ....

3. won't ....

4. she's ....

5. didn't ....

For Questions 6–10, write a contraction to replace the underlined words.

6. <u>We will</u> go to the beach when it's hot. ....

7. The children <u>are not</u> going to the circus. ....

8. I <u>have not</u> seen his new car yet. ....

9. <u>She is</u> going to the shop to buy ice-cream. ....

10. Molly <u>cannot</u> go to school because she is sick. ....

My score: $\dfrac{\quad}{10}$

My time: ....
                                    minutes   seconds

Minute 86

Name: .... Date: ....

For **Questions 1–4**, *circle the compound word in each sentence.*

1. We found lots of seashells at the beach.

2. I put the letter in the postbox.

3. Sam drank a banana milkshake.

4. My parents are painting my bedroom pink.

For **Questions 5–10**, *use the words in the box to write compound words on the lines below. Use each word only once.*

5. ....

6. ....

7. ....

8. ....

9. ....

10. ....

key	fast
way	corn
light	break
rail	bin
dust	sun
board	pop

My score: _____ / **10**

My time: ....
minutes   seconds

Minute 87

Name: ....   Date: ....

Write S if the pairs of words are synonyms (mean the same thing)
or A if they are antonyms (mean the opposite).

1. jog   run   ....

2. wrong   right   ....

3. thin   thick   ....

4. bright   smart   ....

5. happy   cheerful   ....

6. no-one   everyone   ....

7. funny   silly   ....

8. early   late   ....

9. sleep   rest   ....

10. open   close   ....

My score: ____
10

My time: ....
                 minutes   seconds

Minute 88

Name: .... Date: ....

For Questions 1–5, circle the correct meaning for each underlined word.

1. The dog bite on my leg is very <u>painful</u>.
   (a) full of pain   (b) one who is in pain

2. We learned what <u>uneven</u> numbers are in maths class.
   (a) even again   (b) not even

3. The <u>dancer</u> got a new pair of ballet slippers.
   (a) dance again   (b) a person who dances

4. I have to <u>rewrite</u> my messy homework.
   (a) write again   (b) full of writing

5. The baby's birth was a <u>joyful</u> event.
   (a) one who has joy   (b) full of joy

For Questions 6–10, use the words in the box to best complete the story.

Paul the Great is our classroom magician. The tricks

he can do are truly **6.** ....! One minute
he has a rabbit in his hat, and then it suddenly

7. .... into thin air. When Paul the Great

taps the hat again, the rabbit **8.** ....

When I was his magician's **9.** ...., I tried
to learn all his tricks. But Paul the Great does his tricks

too **10.** .... for anyone to learn them.

disappears
reappears
quickly
magical
helper

My score: _____ / **10**   **My time:** ....
                                              minutes   seconds

www.prim-ed.com   Prim-Ed Publishing®

Minute 89

Name: ....   Date: ....

For Questions 1–6, write the words in the box in alphabetical order.

| shells | beach | water | sand | umbrella | towel |

1. ....

2. ....

3. ....

4. ....

5. ....

6. ....

For Questions 7–10, write each set of words in alphabetical order.

7. blue, black, bleed   ....

8. champ, cheap, chirp   ....

9. stripe, struck, strong   ....

10. breathe, brain, bring   ....

My score: $\dfrac{}{10}$ **My time:** ....

minutes   seconds

Name: .... **Date:** ....

For Questions 1–5, write each underlined noun as a possessive noun.

1. <u>Kaila</u> backpack is pink and green. ....

2. The <u>boy</u> history project is almost done. ....

3. <u>Amy</u> favourite watch is on the desk. ....

4. The <u>baby</u> parents are taking her to the zoo. ....

5. <u>Ryan</u> adventure holiday was fun. ....

For Questions 6–10, circle the correct possessive noun in each sentence.

6. The (cakes, cake's) frosting is melting in the sun.

7. The (pianos, piano's) colour is a dark brown.

8. The (cars, car's) brakes need to be checked.

9. (Brenda's, Brenda) keys are locked in the car.

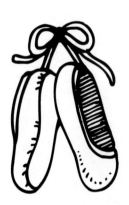

10. The little (girl, girl's) ballet slippers were too small.

My score:
$$\frac{}{10}$$

My time: ....
minutes   seconds

Name: .... **Date:** ....

Circle the correct article in each sentence.

1. I am eating (a, an, the) slice of vegetarian pizza.

2. (A, An, The) clock on the wall stopped.

3. We saw (a, an, the) elephant and a tiger at the zoo.

4. Tina wishes she had (a, an, the) little sister or brother.

5. (A, An, The) apple a day is good for your body.

6. Jarvis ate all of (a, an, the) apple crumble.

7. I like (a, an, the) new teacher we have this year.

8. Don's maths test lasted (a, an, the) hour.

9. Did you know that (a, an, the) dog could
   live 20 years?

10. We saw (a, an, the) emu at the zoo.

My score: _____

10

My time: ....
         minutes   seconds

Minute 92

Name: .... **Date:** ....

Circle the correct word in each sentence.

1. Jane (leaved, left) her hockey stick at home.

2. The running team (ran, runned) one kilometre for practice.

3. The (goose, geese) fly south for the winter.

4. Those shoes are too small for my (feet, foot).

5. The (person, people) are talking too loudly.

6. The birds (fly, flies) high up in the sky.

7. Bobby (watches, watch) his dad fix the car.

8. The man is cutting (a, an) branch off of the tree.

9. Steve (was, were) the first person to get to school.

10. (We, us) are going to the park to play football.

My score: $\dfrac{}{10}$ **My time:** ....
minutes   seconds

Name: .... **Date:** ....

Circle the incorrect word in each sentence and write it correctly on the line.

1. The puppys are fighting over the bone.   ....

2. Mike was'nt happy with his results.   ....

3. My mum is taking we to the cinema.   ....

4. I is going to make pancakes for breakfast.   ....

5. Mrs watson was my teacher last year.   ....

6. Lena go to dance practice every day.   ....

7. We live at 22 Hawk St in manchester.   ....

8. Thomas are outside playing with his neighbour.   ....

9. The boys looked for their cat, fluffy, all day.   ....

10. Samantha can read much fast than I can.   ....

My score: _____
10

My time: ....
minutes   seconds

Name: .... **Date:** ....

For Questions 1–4, circle the incorrect words in each sentence and then write the entire sentence correctly on the line.
(**Hint**: Each sentence has two incorrect words or groups of words.)

1. Mr smith came home with two puppys for his kids.

   ....

2. They is going to australia for a month.

   ....

3. mrs Smith wants to shop in all the centre's many shop.

   ....

4. Mr Smith and ralph want to rides all of the show's rides.

   ....

For Questions 5–10, circle the correct word in each sentence.

5. Patty and Lauren (want, wants) to see a film.

6. They are looking forward to their first (plane, plain) ride.

7. Please raise your (right, write) hand.

8. The dog (runned, ran) around the tree.

9. I (couldn't, coulnd't) decide whether or not to order cake or ice-cream.

10. (She, Her) mother is taking us to the cinema after school.

My score: _____
10

My time: ....
minutes   seconds

Minute 95

Name: .... Date: ....

**Read the story and circle the 10 words that are incorrect.
Write them correctly on the lines below.**

Today in class us learned that a verb is a action word. Mrs

thompson ask each pupil to pull an action word out of a hat and

act it out in front of the class. sallys word were dance. She done a

ballet step she had learned in ballet class. My word was clap. The

pupils guessed my action write away. My best friend, john, skipped

around the room. everyone was laughing. We had fun acting out

our action words.

1. ....   6. ....

2. ....   7. ....

3. ....   8. ....

4. ....   9. ....

5. ....   10. ....

My score: ___
10

My time: ....
minutes   seconds

Minute 96

9
8
7
6

Name: .... Date: ....

For Questions 1–3, rewrite the sentences in the correct word order.

1. Loudly barked at the man the dog.

   ....

2. The boy quickly up the stairs ran.

   ....

3. Towards prey tiger the moved slowly its.

   ....

For Questions 4–10, circle the incorrect word in each sentence and write it correctly on the line.

4. There was'n't any bread left to make
   a sandwich.   ....

5. Tosha loves to swam in the pool.   ....

6. Flynn cant reach the biscuit jar.   ....

7. I eight apple and rhubarb pie for dessert. ....

8. The wind blue my hat away.   ....

9. Them are coming to the library with us.   ....

10. I are working hard on my English test.   ....

My score: _____
10

My time: ....
minutes   seconds

Minute 97

9
8
7
6

Name: .... **Date:** ....

Write N *if the sentence is missing a noun or* V *if it is missing a verb.*
(**Hint**: Write a word to complete each sentence. Then see if it is a noun or a verb.)

1. My teacher .... around the room.   ....

2. I had fun eating lunch with my .... today.   ....

3. The dog was covered in .... after the rain.   ....

4. The wedding .... is now too small for her
   to wear.   ....

5. We had fun .... in the rain yesterday.   ....

6. Martin and .... take their dog to the vet.   ....

7. I .... up my bed every morning before school...............

8. The fluffy clouds .... so high in the sky.   ....

9. Many .... were at the parade.   ....

10. Chelsea .... every Saturday morning.   ....

My score: _____
10

My time: ....
minutes   seconds

Name: .... **Date:** ....

For Questions 1–3, circle two nouns and underline one verb in each sentence.

1. The girls often play in the park.

2. Jasmine always does her homework.

3. Sometimes, Sajit eats a whole hamburger.

For Questions 4–10, circle the sentences that are written correctly.

4. (a) Tyler loves to go to his grandparents' home.
   (b) tyler loves to go to his grandparents' home.

5. (a) They have a big apple tree in the garden.
   (b) Them have a big apple tree in the garden.

6. (a) We have ate new pupils this year.
   (b) We have eight new pupils this year.

7. (a) Olivia is the cuter puppy at the dog show.
   (b) Olivia is the cutest puppy at the dog show.

8. (a) Joey often climbs to the top of the tree in his garden.
   (b) Joey often climb to the top of the tree in his garden.

9. (a) Maria asked her parents if she could go with they.
   (b) Maria asked her parents if she could go with them.

10. (a) Those men are helping my mother with the car.
    (b) Those mans are helping my mother with the car.

My score: _____

10

My time: ....
                        minutes   seconds

Name: .... **Date:** ....

Write the correct present- and past-tense form in each sentence.

Present tense	Past tense
1. She .... **(wrote writes)** on the board.	**2.** I .... my **(read reading)** nanna a letter.
3. My dad is .... **(flew flying)** that plane.	**4.** The bird .... **(flew flying)** into the window.
5. I .... too **(speak spoke)** loudly sometimes.	**6.** A famous artist .... at **(speak spoke)** my school.
7. Paul .... the **(throws threw)** rubbish away for his mum.	**8.** He .... my **(throws threw)** favourite toy in the pool!
9. Julio is .... **(read reading)** the newspaper.	**10.** I .... a **(read reading)** funny story yesterday.

My score: _____
10

My time: ....
minutes   seconds

Minute 100

Name: .... **Date:** ....

For Questions 1–5, circle the adjectives in the sentences.

(**Hint**: Each sentence has two adjectives to circle.)

1. The bright pupils solved the difficult problem.

2. My favourite cousins live in sunny Spain.

3. The grey dog loves his caring family.

4. I am going to wear my new pink dress on Sunday.

5. I have twelve red roses to give to you.

For Questions 6–10, circle the incorrect word in each sentence and then write it correctly on the line.

6. I doesn't have any money for lunch. ....

7. Why are he going to the office? ....

8. Regina dropped the book on she foot. ....

9. Me can't surf very well. ....

10. Carrie luggage was lost at the airport. ....

My score: _____
10

My time: ....
minutes   seconds

Minute answer key

Minute 1
1. b
2. a
3. b
4. a
5. Complete
6. Incomplete
7. Complete
8. Complete
9. Incomplete
10. Complete

Minute 2
1. b
2. a
3. a
4. b
5. a
6. The film was funny.
7. I ride on my bike.
8. The cat sleeps a lot.
9. The ice-cream is sweet.
10. The puppy was lost.

Minute 3
1. A
2. T
3. E
4. A
5. T
6. T
7. A
8. E
9. T
10. T

Minute 4
1. b
2. a
3. a
4. a
5. b
6. b
7. b
8. a
9. a
10. b

Minute 5
1. I
2. We
3. Sarah's
4. Wednesday
5. My
6. October
7. Max
8. Greece
9. They
10. Every

Minute 6
1. ?
2. !
3. !
4. .
5. .
6. ?
7. !
8. .
9. .
10. ?

Minute 7
Order of answers may vary.
1. pupil
2. sister
3. teacher
4. umpire
5. park
6. school
7. lake
8. phone
9. flower
10. radio

Minute 8
1. girls, park
2. Brandon, books
3. Apples, grapes
4. Marie, Tina
5. Tom, cake
6. beach, summer
7. Chris, dog
8. dog, cat
9. clouds, sky
10. Mr Manson, teacher

Minute 9
1. Meg, Amy
2. Charlie
3. Nick, Mitch
4. Lucky
5. Punka
6. Timothy
7. Nicole
8. Megan, Madison
9. Mozart
10. Bubbles

Minute 10
1. b
2. a
3. b
4. a
5. b
6. a
7. b
8. a
9. a
10. b

Minute 11
1. Uncle Herbert
2. Dr Dawson
3. Mrs Gomez
4. Police Officer Edwards
5. Grandma Rose
6. c
7. a
8. b
9. c
10. b

Minute 12
1. Erskineville Secondary School
2. Parker Garden Centre
3. Burger Express
4. Pets 4 All
5. Barcelona, Spain
6. Rose Park
7. Rope Walk Centre
8. Australia
9. Strath Creek Library
10. Howson Street

Minute 13
1. C
2. I
3. C
4. a
5. b
6. T
7. E
8. A
9. E
10. A

Minute 14
1. How are you?
2. My desk is dirty.
3. The clock is black.
4. Wow, she's tall!
5. I play the piano.
6. No
7. No
8. Yes
9. Yes
10. No

Minute 15
Order of answers for 1.–6. may vary.
1. nurse
2. singer
3. hospital
4. bedroom
5. ring
6. brush
7. firefighter, kitten
8. flowers, garden
9. dog, toy
10. nurse, cut

Minute 16
1. Thomas
2. Bracknell
3. Cardiff
4. Bristol
5. London
6. Johnny's
7. Greene
8. Chi
9. Hua
10. Jennifer

Minute 17
The following 10 words should be circled:
1. chew
2. swim
3. clap
4. type
5. dance
6. smell
7. walk
8. eat
9. jump
10. drive

Minute 18
1. feeds
2. barks
3. play
4. reads
5. walked
6. swam
7. slides
8. rode
9. chirp
10. types

Minute 19
1. jogged
2. played
3. helps
4. have
5. was
6. danced
7. cried
8. licks
9. pulls
10. chews

Minute 20
1. scratches
2. scratched
3. yawn
4. yawned
5. write
6. wrote
7. is
8. raked
9. look
10. bowled

Minute answer key

Minute 21
1. is
2. are
3. am
4. is
5. is
6. is
7. is
8. am
9. are
10. is

Minute 22
1. was
2. was
3. were
4. was
5. were
6. was
7. were
8. was
9. were
10. was

Minute 23
1. have
2. has
3. have or had
4. have
5. has or had
6. have
7. has
8. had
9. had
10. have

Minute 24
1. grey
2. sweet
3. five
4. pretty
5. sour
6. tiny
7. green
8. loud
9. mean
10. little

Minute 25
1. taller
2. fastest
3. slowest
4. shorter
5. brighter
6. smartest
7. nicest
8. bigger
9. cleaner
10. deepest

Minute 26
1. Exeter, Devon
2. Newcastle, United Kingdom
3. Paris, France
4. 121 Huston Drive, Cork, Ireland
5. 71 Tyne Way, Glasgow
6. Obama, left
7. Tuffin, BA
8. Wallis, CEO
9. Norton, JP,
10. Sampson, Member of the Legislative Assembly,

Minute 27
1. read, skate
2. football, rugby
3. crisps, popcorn
4. lions, tigers
5. b
6. b
7. b
8. b
9. a
10. b

Minute 28
The following 10 words should be circled:
1. went
2. saw
3. drew
4. told
5. run
6. play
7. ate
8. rode
9. write
10. read

Minute 29
1. No
2. Yes
3. No
4. Past
5. Present
6. Present
7. Past
8. was
9. is
10. had

Minute 30
1. smart
2. fastest
3. red
4. fresh
5. yellow
6. prettiest
7. beautiful
8. healthier
9. best
10. longer

Minute 31
1. pancakes, eggs
2. Poole, Dorset
3. Parliament, London, England
4. a
5. b
6. b
7. Yes
8. Yes
9. Yes
10. No

Minute 32
1. I
2. me
3. me
4. I
5. me
6. me
7. I
8. I
9. me
10. me

Minute 33
1. No
2. Yes
3. No
4. No
5. Yes
6. He
7. She
8. her
9. him
10. She

Minute 34
1. We
2. us
3. We
4. us
5. We
6. We
7. us
8. we
9. We
10. us

Minute 35
1. They
2. them
3. They
4. They
5. them
6. No
7. Yes
8. Yes
9. Yes
10. No

Minute 36
1. dresses
2. cats
3. girls
4. beaches
5. foxes
6. ponies
7. friends
8. toys
9. brothers
10. cities

Minute 37
1. ponies
2. babies
3. trucks
4. foxes
5. glasses
6. pencils
7. apples
8. boxes
9. boys
10. classes

Minute 38
1. baby's
2. Nicole's
3. painter's
4. clock's
5. city's
6. a giraffe's neck
7. the dog's mat
8. the turtle's shell
9. the car's tyres
10. Ming's dress

Minute 39
1. Don't
2. I'm
3. can't
4. haven't
5. shouldn't
6. No
7. Yes
8. No
9. Yes
10. Yes

Minute 40
1. haven't
2. wasn't
3. She's
4. I'll
5. didn't
6. can not
7. is not
8. do not
9. has not
10. should not

www.prim-ed.com — Prim-Ed Publishing®

Minute answer key

Minute 41
1. doghouse
2. raincoat
3. sunglasses
4. newspaper
5–10. afternoon, toothpaste, seahorse, watermelon, grandfather, homework

Minute 42
1. backyard
2. outside
3. playground
4. basketball
5. Yes
6. No
7. No
8. Yes
9. Yes
10. No

Minute 43
1. She
2. They
3. him
4. He
5. She
6. us
7. He
8. They
9. her
10. I

Minute 44
1. carrots
2. families
3. couches
4. classes
5. axes
6. dog's
7. cake's
8. children's
9. chair's
10. computer's

Minute 45
1. he's
2. doesn't
3. aren't
4. you're
5. you'll
6. would have
7. will not
8. is not
9. did not
10. must not

Minute 46
1. skyscrapers
2. earthworm
3. peppermints
4. snowman
5. wristwatch
6. sunflowers
7. birdhouse
8. postcard
9. rattlesnake
10. homework

Minute 47
1. angry
2. scream
3. beautiful
4. hop
5. sleepy
6. small
7. hates
8. buddy
9. unhappy
10. completed

Minute 48
1. quiet, silent
2. old, ancient
3. talk, speak
4. rich, wealthy
5. No
6. No
7. No
8. No
9. Yes
10. Yes

Minute 49
1. go
2. up
3. sit
4. asleep
5. forget
6. run
7. dull
8. quiet
9. huge
10. neat

Minute 50
1. late
2. hot
3. right
4. terrible
5. dry
6. pretty
7. down
8. fast
9. small *or* little
10. low

Minute 51
1. sun
2. see
3. piece
4. prey
5. bee
6. blue
7. Yes
8. No
9. Yes
10. No

Minute 52
1. b
2. a
3. b
4. b
5. b
6. b
7. c
8. d
9. b
10. a

Minute 53
1. unhappy
2. rewrite
3. unhealthy
4. refill
5. unlucky
6. c
7. d
8. a
9. e
10. b

Minute 54
1. helper
2. hurtful
3. player
4. helpful
5. playful
6. painter: one who paints
7. colourful: full of colour
8. cheerful: full of cheer
9. teacher: one who teaches
10. hopeful: full of hope

Minute 55
1. duck
2. five
3. grapes
4. job
5. skate
6. weather
7. Yes
8. Yes
9. No
10. Yes

Minute 56
1. shake, slide, snap
2. already, any, apple
3. grape, great, grew
4. draw, drink, drum
5. handsome
6. head
7. heat
8. home
9. house
10. hum

Minute 57
1. S
2. A
3. A
4. S
5. A
6. S
7. A
8. S
9. A
10. S

Minute 58
1. sun
2. made
3. plane
4. meet
5. write
6. new
7. c
8. a
9. d
10. b

Minute 59
1. S
2. P
3. S
4. S
5. P
6. replay
7. driver
8. unpack
9. beautiful
10. reread

Minute 60
1. No
2. Yes
3. Yes
4. No
5. Yes
6. No
7. Yes
8. Yes
9. No
10. Yes

Minute answer key

Minute 61
1. an
2. a
3. a
4. An
5. a
6. a
7. an
8. a
9. an
10. a

Minute 62
1. the
2. a
3. The
4. an or the
5. a
6. the
7. a
8. the
9. the
10. An

Minute 63
1. fed
2. threw
3. wrote
4. made
5. took
6. ran
7. froze
8. stood
9. left
10. read

Minute 64
1. hold
2. take
3. catch
4. fight
5. wear
6. run
7. took
8. grew
9. swam
10. sold

Minute 65
1. calves
2. men
3. women
4. mice
5. loaves
6. knives
7. children
8. leaves
9. feet
10. hooves

Minute 66
1. geese
2. people
3. shelves
4. knives
5. loaves
6. teeth
7. men
8. children
9. people
10. leaves

Minute 67
1. quickly
2. fast
3. easily
4. tomorrow
5. on Saturday
6. yesterday
7. near my house
8. outside
9. above our house
10. under the table

Minute 68
1. slowly
2. neatly
3. safely
4. carefully
5. quickly
6. sadly
7. when
8. how
9. how
10. where

Minute 69
1. brushes
2. ate
3. opens
4. rode
5. scratched
6. wrote
7. boys
8. apple
9. flowers
10. children

Minute 70
1. No
2. Yes
3. No
4. Yes
5. No
6. children, play
7. chair, fell
8. ladies, walk
9. wash, plates
10. kids, helped

Minute 71
1. Yes
2. No
3. No
4. No
5. No
6. Yes
7. No
8. Yes
9. Yes
10. No

Minute 72
1. tore
2. thought
3. swam
4. froze
5. flew
6. mice
7. feet
8. wolves
9. fish
10. deer

Minute 73
1. lazily
2. anywhere
3. closer
4. safely
5. every day
6. across
7. softly
8. angrily
9. neatly
10. easily

Minute 74
1. No
2. No
3. Yes
4. No
5. Yes
6. No
7. Yes
8. No
9. No
10. Yes

Minute 75
1. C
2. I
3. C
4. I
5. No
6. No
7. Yes
8. b
9. a
10. b

Minute 76
1. Jamie, Melville
2. Her, Ms Rice
3. Cindy, Marcia
4. We, Ocean World
5. My, I
6. My, Kyle
7. Next, Luna Park
8. Our, Butler Road
9. My, Tuesday
10. Mr Turner, Allen

Minute 77
1. ?
2. .
3. ?
4. .
5. !
6. A
7. E
8. T
9. A
10. E

Minute 78
Possible answers
include:
1. Nouns: firefighter, cat, house
   Verb: saved
2. Nouns: flowers, water, sunlight
   Verb: need
3. Nouns: toy, mud, garden
   Verb: got
4. Nouns: nurse, bandage, cut
   Verb: put
5. Nouns: Greg, dog, bath
   Verb: washes
6. Nouns: Tony, water, sister
   Verb: sprays
7. Nouns: child, car, street
   Verb: ran
8. Nouns: friends, games, school
   Verb: played
9. Nouns: Susie, books, holidays
   Verb: reads
10. Nouns: teacher, test, morning
    Verb: marked

www.prim-ed.com Prim-Ed Publishing®

Minute answer key

Minute 79
1. girls
2. ditches
3. babies
4. mice
5. buses
6. sisters
7. puppies
8. classes
9. boxes
10. flowers

Minute 80
1. Past
2. Past
3. Present
4. Present
5. No
6. No
7. Yes
8. No
9. Yes
10. No

Minute 81
1. orange
2. sad
3. strong
4. sweet
5. sour
6. bitter
7. spicy
8. purple
9. fresh
10. handsome

Minute 82
1. No
2. Yes
3. No
4. No
5. Yes
6. am
7. is
8. has
9. were
10. are

Minute 83
1. Yes
2. No
3. Yes
4. Yes
5. No
6. a
7. a
8. a
9. a
10. b

Minute 84
1. No
2. No
3. Yes
4. Yes
5. Yes
6. No
7. No
8. Yes
9. Yes
10. Yes

Minute 85
1. should not
2. do not
3. will not
4. she is
5. did not
6. We'll
7. aren't
8. haven't
9. She's
10. can't

Minute 86
1. seashells
2. postbox
3. milkshake
4. bedroom
5–10. keyboard, railway, sunlight, popcorn, dustbin, breakfast

Minute 87
1. S
2. A
3. A
4. S
5. S
6. A
7. S
8. A
9. S
10. A

Minute 88
1. a
2. b
3. b
4. a
5. b
6. magical
7. disappears
8. reappears
9. helper
10. quickly

Minute 89
1. beach
2. sand
3. shells
4. towel
5. umbrella
6. water
7. black, bleed, blue
8. champ, cheap, chirp
9. stripe, strong, struck
10. brain, breathe, bring

Minute 90
1. Kaila's
2. boy's
3. Amy's
4. baby's
5. Ryan's
6. cake's
7. piano's
8. car's
9. Brenda's
10. girl's

Minute 91
1. a or the
2. The
3. an
4. a
5. An
6. the
7. the
8. an
9. a
10. an

Minute 92
1. left
2. ran
3. geese
4. feet
5. people
6. fly
7. watches
8. a
9. was
10. We

Minute 93
1. puppies
2. wasn't
3. us
4. am
5. Watson
6. goes
7. Manchester
8. is
9. Fluffy
10. faster

Minute 94
1. Smith, puppies
2. are, Australia
3. Mrs, shops
4. Ralph, ride
5. want
6. plane
7. right
8. ran
9. couldn't
10. Her

Minute 95
1. we
2. an
3. Thompson
4. asked
5. Sally's
6. was
7. did
8. right
9. John
10. Everyone

Minute 96
1. The dog barked loudly at the man. OR The dog loudly barked at the man.
2. The boy ran quickly up the stairs. OR The boy quickly ran up the stairs.
3. The tiger moved slowly towards its prey. OR The tiger slowly moved toward its prey.
4. wasn't
5. swim
6. can't
7. ate
8. blew
9. They
10. am

Minute 97
1. V
2. N
3. N
4. N
5. V
6. N
7. V
8. V
9. N
10. V

Minute 98
1. Nouns: girls, park
   Verb: play
2. Nouns: Jasmine, homework
   Verb: does
3. Nouns: Sajit, hamburger
   Verb: eats
4. a
5. a
6. b
7. b
8. a
9. b
10. a

Minute 99
1. writes
2. wrote
3. flying
4. flew
5. speak
6. spoke
7. throws
8. threw
9. reading
10. read

Minute 100
1. bright, difficult
2. favourite, sunny
3. grey, caring
4. new, pink
5. twelve, red
6. don't
7. is
8. her
9. I
10. Carrie's